THE
DAILY DOZEN

Story by Susan Dickerson

Pictures by James Graham Hale

HOUGHTON MIFFLIN   BOSTON • MORRIS PLAINS, NJ

California   •   Colorado   •   Georgia   •   Illinois   •   New Jersey   •   Texas

It was six days before the
Boomtown Parade. Everyone had
to practice marching.

On Monday, 12 police officers marched in 1 long line of 12.

Jimmy said,

"Let's march that way."

On Tuesday, 12 librarians marched in 2 lines of 6.

Rita said,

"Let's march that way."

On Wednesday, 12 fire fighters marched in 3 lines of 4.

13

Keisha said,

"Let's march that way."

On Thursday, 12 scouts
marched in 4 lines of 3.

Carmen said,

"Let's march that way."

19

On Friday, 12 musicians marched in 6 lines of 2.

Bobby said,

"Let's march that way."

On Saturday, 12 hospital workers marched in 12 short lines of 1.

Jaime said,

"Let's march that way."

On Sunday, everyone marched
in the Boomtown Parade.

29

And the clowns marched
the same way as

the police officers,

the librarians,

the fire fighters,

the scouts,

the musicians,

and the hospital workers.